100 "End Game" Chess Puzzles for Beginners (Rating 900-1200)

100 real-life chess tactics puzzles for beginners to make you a better player

100 "End Game" Chess Puzzles for Beginners (Rating 900-1200)

Published by **www.chess-books.co.uk**

ISBN: 978-1-78933-274-2

Table of Contents

Introduction

Hi! I'm The Chess Puzzler and I'm here to make you a better chess player.

Chess puzzles are an essential part of your development as a player and contribute a massively to your tactical understanding of the game. Even Grandmasters devote time every day to solving chess puzzles to keep them sharp and improve their chess "intuition".

Right from the opening and on into the middle and end game, strong chess players always have an eye out for opportunities to use *tactics* and will quickly recognize positions on the board that are similar to set-ups they have studied in tactical puzzles. Building this intuition quickly helps you spot unexpected *smiting* moves and longer combinations that your opponent hasn't seen. They will save you time on the board by teaching you where to look, and help build the kind of vision that will make your rating skyrocket.

However, a word of caution! While solving chess puzzles will absolutely improve your calculation and strategy skills, you need to also develop a feel for *when* to start calculating in a real game because most games you play will begin with a *quiet* position. For that reason you should concurrently develop your understanding of *positional* chess which breaks down into building strong openings and knowing how to develop your pieces so that they work together on the board. Studying chess tactics is essential but knowing when to start looking for them in an actual game is an important skill too, otherwise you'll just run out your clock.

As a rule of thumb, you should spend more time calculating tactics in a game when there is *tension* on the board. Often (but of course, not exclusively) this is when the opening is complete and opposing pieces are starting to come into contact.

The types of puzzles that will improve your game most quickly are the ones that have been played by real people (every puzzle in this book has been taken from an actual game), and you should steer away from complicated imaginary positions that wouldn't appear in a real life. They can be fun, but you want to focus on plausible chess situations. It's all about building great and relevant chess intuition that you can on the board.

Get Free Chess Puzzles

If you want to get better quickly, you can download our free book of 300 mixed chess puzzles from:

www.chess-books.co.uk/free

or by scanning this QR code with your smart phone

You'll get 300 mixed chess puzzles that start from beginner and move right through to fiendish levels!

All you need to do is fill in the form and we'll email you your book immediately.

Download it now!

The Puzzles

Ready to dive in?

The chess puzzles in this book are all taken from real-life games and are solved by gaining a decisive material or positional advantage in the end game.

The solutions are written on the page directly after the puzzles for easy reference, but no peaking!

The best way to train your brain is to try and solve a puzzle in its entirety before looking at any part of the solution.

For best results:

Set up the position on a physical chess board and give yourself 10 minutes to explore the first three strongest looking candidate moves. These include moves that *force* a response from your opponent, such as checks or the potential capture of an undefended piece.

For each move, explore the opponent's possible responses and then calculate what subsequent move would be strongest for you in return. This should lead you towards the solution.

Spend more time exploring the moves that look to give a more positive outcome, but don't forget that the best moves aren't always the most intuitive ones – at least not yet!

If none of your initial moves offer an immediately positive outcome, then look for a positional move that help develop your pieces so you can gain an advantage or make subsequent forcing move.

Remember that forks, skewers, decoys, double attacks, and mating patterns are all things you should be looking out for when learning to solve chess puzzles.

1 - White to Move

2 - White to Move

3 - Black to Move

4 - Black to Move

Solutions

1) 1. Ne7+ Kh7 2. Nxg6

2) 1. c7 Qxc7 2. Rxc7

3) 1... Kxg5

4) 1... Nd3+ 2. Ke2 Nxb2

5 - Black to Move

6 - White to Move

7 - White to Move

8 - White to Move

Solutions

5) 1... c3 2. g8=Q c2+

6) 1. Bxd7+ Kxd7 2. Rxe8 Kxe8 3. Bxc7

7) 1. Bd4+ Bf6 2. Bxf6#

8) 1. Rxb6+ axb6 2. a7

9 - Black to Move

10 - White to Move

11 - White to Move

12 - Black to Move

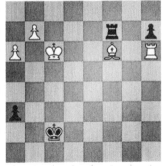

Solutions

9) 1... d4+ 2. Kd2 dxe3+

10) 1. Qf7+ Kh8 2. Qf8+ Rxf8 3. Rxf8#

11) 1. Rh7+ Kf8 2. Rh8+ Ke7 3. Rxb8

12) 1... Rxc3+ 2. Rxc3 a1=Q

13 - White to Move

14 - White to Move

15 - White to Move

16 - White to Move

Solutions

13) 1. Rxh6+ gxh6 2. g7+ Kh7 3. g8=Q#

14) 1. e6+ Ke7 2. exd7

15) 1. Rc8+ Ne8 2. Rxe8#

16) 1. Bxg2 Nxg2 2. a5 Kg3 3. a6

17 - Black to Move

18 - White to Move

19 - Black to Move

20 - Black to Move

Solutions

17) 1... Ng3+ 2. Kg1 Nxe4

18) 1. Kxf3

19) 1... Qxe1+

20) 1... Rxb5

21 - White to Move

22 - Black to Move

23 - White to Move

24 - Black to Move

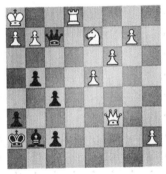

Solutions

21) 1. Ra6+ Ke7 2. Rxa7+

22) 1... Kg2 2. Rxf4 h1=Q

23) 1. Nxf1 Nxf1 2. h6 Ke6 3. h7

24) 1... Qxe1+ 2. Nf1 Qxf1#

25 - Black to Move

26 - White to Move

27 - White to Move

28 - Black to Move

Solutions

25) 1... Bxe7 2. a7 Nb6

26) 1. Re8+ Kb7 2. Rxd7

27) 1. e6+ Kxe6 2. Rxb5

28) 1... Qxg4 2. hxg4 Rxe1 3. Rxe1 Rxe1+

29 - White to Move

30 - White to Move

31 - White to Move

32 - Black to Move

Solutions

29) 1. Rd8+ Qe8 2. Rxe8+

30) 1. exf7+ Qxf7 2. Rxe7 Rxe7 3. Qxe7 Qxe7 4. Rxe7

31) 1. Rxf4

32) 1... e2 2. h7 e1=Q+

33 - Black to Move

34 - White to Move

35 - Black to Move

36 - White to Move

Solutions

33) 1... Nf2#

34) 1. Qh4+ Qxh4+ 2. Kxh4 Kg6 3. a4 Kf6 4. a5

35) 1... hxg4+ 2. Kxg4 Rh4#

36) 1. Ke4 Rf1 2. Rxc6+

37 - White to Move

38 - White to Move

39 - Black to Move

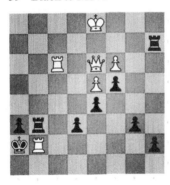

40 - Black to Move

Solutions

37) 1. e4 Kxb3 2. e5

38) 1. Ra8#

39) 1... Kxg7 2. Qf1 Ra1+ 3. Kd2 Rxf1

40) 1... Re1+ 2. Kf3 Rf1+ 3. Ke3 Rxf7

41 - Black to Move

42 - White to Move

43 - White to Move

44 - White to Move

Solutions

41) 1... Ne3+ 2. fxe3 Qf1+ 3. Kh2 Rf2+ 4. Qxf2 Qxf2+

42) 1. e6 Kxe4 2. e7

43) 1. d5 Kxe3 2. d6

44) 1. Qxh7+ Kxh7 2. Rh3#

45 - Black to Move

46 - White to Move

47 - White to Move

48 - White to Move

Solutions

45) 1... Ng4+ 2. Kg2 Ne3+ 3. Rxe3 dxe3

46) 1. Rf1+ Kg6 2. Rxf8

47) 1. d7 Kxd7 2. Kxd5

48) 1. Qc6 Qxc6+ 2. Kxc6 Kf2 3. a8=Q

49 - Black to Move

50 - White to Move

51 - Black to Move

52 - Black to Move

Solutions

49) 1... Qc1+ 2. Kh2 Bxf4

50) 1. Rxd8+ Kxd8 2. Rg8+ Ke7 3. Re8#

51) 1... Bxf4 2. Bxf4 Kxf4 3. Kb4 Kxe5

52) 1... g4+ 2. Kxg4 Qh5+ 3. Kh3 Qxf3

53 - White to Move

54 - White to Move

55 - White to Move

56 - Black to Move

Solutions

53) 1. Rc8+ Nxc8 2. Qxc8+ Qd8 3. Qxd8+

54) 1. e5+ Ke7 2. exd6+

55) 1. Rxe8+

56) 1... e2+ 2. Kh1 exf1=Q#

57 - Black to Move

58 - White to Move

59 - Black to Move

60 - Black to Move

Solutions

57) 1... Rh1+ 2. Ke2 Rxe4+

58) 1. Qxa8+ Rf8 2. Bxe6+ Kh8 3. Qxf8#

59) 1... g4+ 2. Kh2 gxf3

60) 1... Qxc2 2. Rxc2 e2 3. Rxe2 Rxe2

61 - White to Move

62 - Black to Move

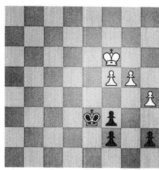

63 - Black to Move

64 - White to Move

Solutions

61) 1. Qh8+ Ke7 2. Qxg7+

62) 1... c5 2. a6 cxb4+

63) 1... Qe1+ 2. Qf1 Bh2+ 3. Kxh2 Qxf1

64) 1. d6 Kg8 2. d7

65 - White to Move

66 - Black to Move

67 - White to Move

68 - Black to Move

Solutions

65) 1. Qxb6+ Qb7 2. Qxd8+

66) 1... hxg2+ 2. Kxg2 Rh2#

67) 1. Ng6+ hxg6 2. Rxe8+ Kh7 3. hxg4

68) 1... Kxh6 2. Kh8 Qd8#

69 - White to Move

70 - Black to Move

71 - Black to Move

72 - Black to Move

Solutions

69) 1. Kb6 Kc8 2. c5 Kb8 3. c6 bxc6 4. Kxc6

70) 1... Qxe1+ 2. Kg2 exd4

71) 1... a2 2. Nd2 a1=Q

72) 1... Rf4+ 2. Ka3 b4+ 3. Kxa4 bxc3+

73 - Black to Move

74 - White to Move

75 - Black to Move

76 - Black to Move

Solutions

73) 1... Rc1+ 2. Rd1 d2+ 3. Kf1 Rxd1#

74) 1. Rxf8+ Kh7 2. Rxe1

75) 1... Qg3+ 2. Kf1 Qxh2

76) 1... Bc3+ 2. Kd3 exf5

77 - White to Move

78 - White to Move

79 - Black to Move

80 - Black to Move

77) 1. Qxf2 Rxf2+ 2. Kxf2

78) 1. Ra8+ Rb8 2. Rxb8+ Kxb8 3. Rxd7

79) 1... Ng3+ 2. Kd3 e4+ 3. Kd2 exf3

80) 1... Be3+ 2. Kb1 Qxe2

81 - White to Move

82 - White to Move

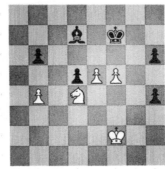

83 - White to Move

84 - White to Move

Solutions

81) 1. Rxe4 dxe4 2. Ke3

82) 1. e6+ Ke7 2. exd7

83) 1. Rxh6+ Kg3 2. Nf1#

84) 1. Rc8+ Rd8 2. Rxd8+ Rg8 3. Rxg8#

85 - Black to Move

86 - Black to Move

87 - Black to Move

88 - Black to Move

Solutions

85) 1... h2 2. Bxh2 Bxh2

86) 1... Ne4+ 2. Ke1 Nxf2+

87) 1... Qh1+ 2. Kg4 Qxh8

88) 1... Qc1+ 2. Qf1 Be3+ 3. Kh1 Qxf1#

89 - White to Move

90 - Black to Move

91 - White to Move

92 - Black to Move

Solutions

89) 1. c6+ Kf7 2. cxd7

90) 1... Nf3+ 2. Kh1 Rd1+ 3. Rg1 Rxg1#

91) 1. Bxc4 Kxc4 2. g4

92) 1... Kh7

93 - White to Move

94 - White to Move

95 - White to Move

96 - White to Move

Solutions

93) 1. Rd7 Qxd7 2. exd7 Rxe4 3. d8=Q

94) 1. Re8+ Kh7 2. Rxf7 Rg1+ 3. Ka2

95) 1. Qe2+ Kf5 2. Qxh5#

96) 1. b7 Rb8 2. Rb6 Kc7 3. Rxe6

97 - White to Move

98 - White to Move

99 - Black to Move

100 - Black to Move

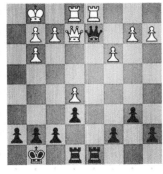

Solutions

97) 1. Ne6+ Kd7 2. Nc5+ Kc6 3. Nxb3

98) 1. Bf5 Qg6 2. Bxg6

99) 1... Nf3+ 2. Kh1 Rxh2#

100)   1... Qxe2 2. Rxe2 Rxd1+

Get Free Chess Puzzles

If you want to get better quickly, you can download our free book of 300 mixed chess puzzles from:

www.chess-books.co.uk/free

or by scanning this QR code with your smart phone

You'll get 300 mixed chess puzzles that start from beginner and move right through to fiendish levels!

All you need to do is fill in the form and we'll email you your book immediately.

Download it now!

Made in the USA
Monee, IL
28 September 2022

14828933R00036